It's Another Ace Book from CGP

It's chock-full of questions that are carefully designed to make sure you know all the _really important stuff_ about Moving and Growing in Year Four Science.

And we've had a really good stab at making it funny — so you'll actually _want to use it_.

Simple as that.

CGP are just the best

The central aim of Coordination Group Publications is to produce top quality books that are carefully written, beautifully presented and marvellously funny — whilst always making sure they exactly cover the National Curriculum for each subject.

And then we supply them to as many people as we possibly can, as _cheaply_ as we possibly can.

Buy our books — they're ace

Contents

Answers to the questions are on the back of the Pull-out Poster in the centre of the book.

Published by Coordination Group Publications Ltd.

Contributors:

Angela Billington   BA (Hons), MPhil

Charley Darbishire BA (Hons)

Chris Dennett   BSc (Hons)

Katherine Stewart   BA (Hons)

Claire Thompson BSc

Tim Wakeling   BA (Hons), GIMA

James Paul Wallis   BEng (Hons)

Andrew Wright   BA (Hons)

ISBN 1 84146 260 8
Groovy website: www.cgpbooks.co.uk
Jolly bits of clipart from CorelDRAW
Printed by Elanders Hindson, Newcastle upon Tyne.

Text, design, layout and original illustrations © Coordination Group Publications Ltd. 2000

Bones Inside You

We're all full of bones — if we didn't have any we'd fall down in a floppy heap. Bones of all different shapes and sizes fit together to make a <u>skeleton</u>.

Q1 Feel your own body to see where some of your bones are and try to draw them on this picture.

You can feel some of your bones in your chest — they're the hard bits. Find some of the big bones in your arms and legs and draw them too.

See what bones you can find in your fingers by feeling them. Draw some of them on this picture.

I like eating bones.

BONEATER

Arnold had loads of bones inside him.

Q2 All the bones in your body go together to make up your skeleton. Take the letters from the diagram of the skeleton below and fit them into this body in the right order.

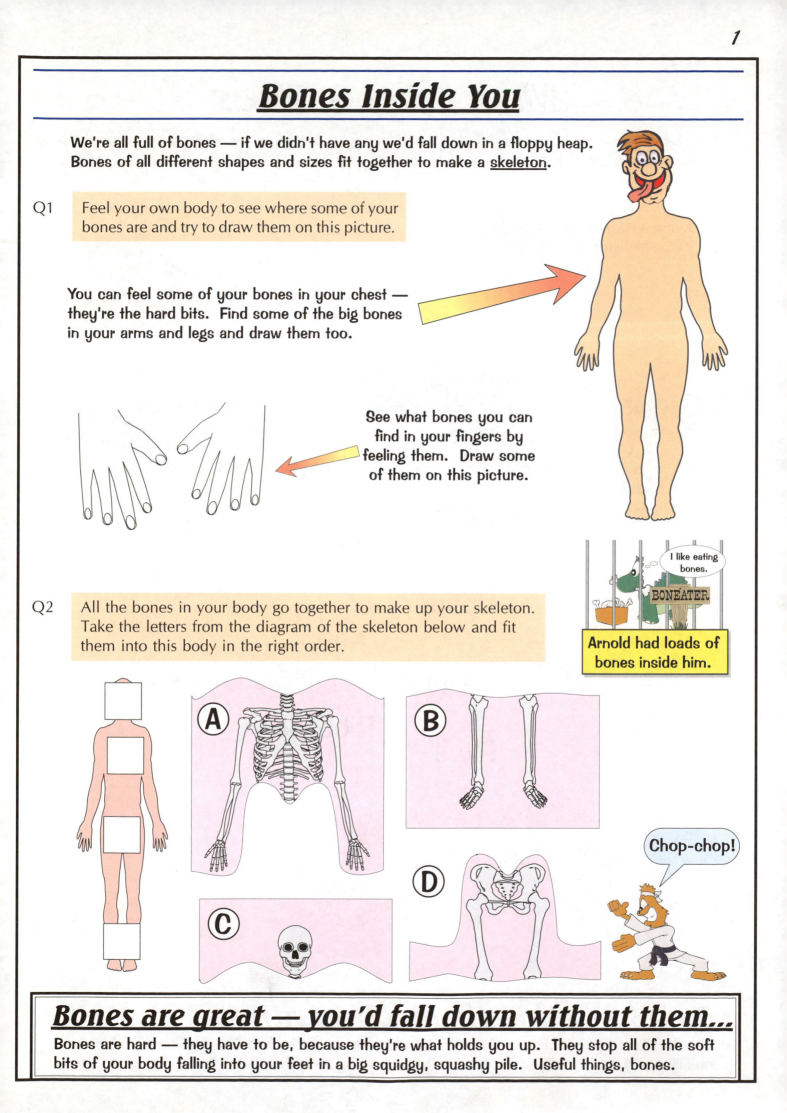

Chop-chop!

Bones are great — you'd fall down without them...

Bones are hard — they have to be, because they're what holds you up. They stop all of the soft bits of your body falling into your feet in a big squidgy, squashy pile. Useful things, bones.

Which Bones Go Where

Each bit of you is made up of a different set of bones. These bones are made to do different things — the bones in your hands are made to hold things, and your spine is made to keep you upright.

Q1 Draw arrows to match the bits of the skeleton to their names.

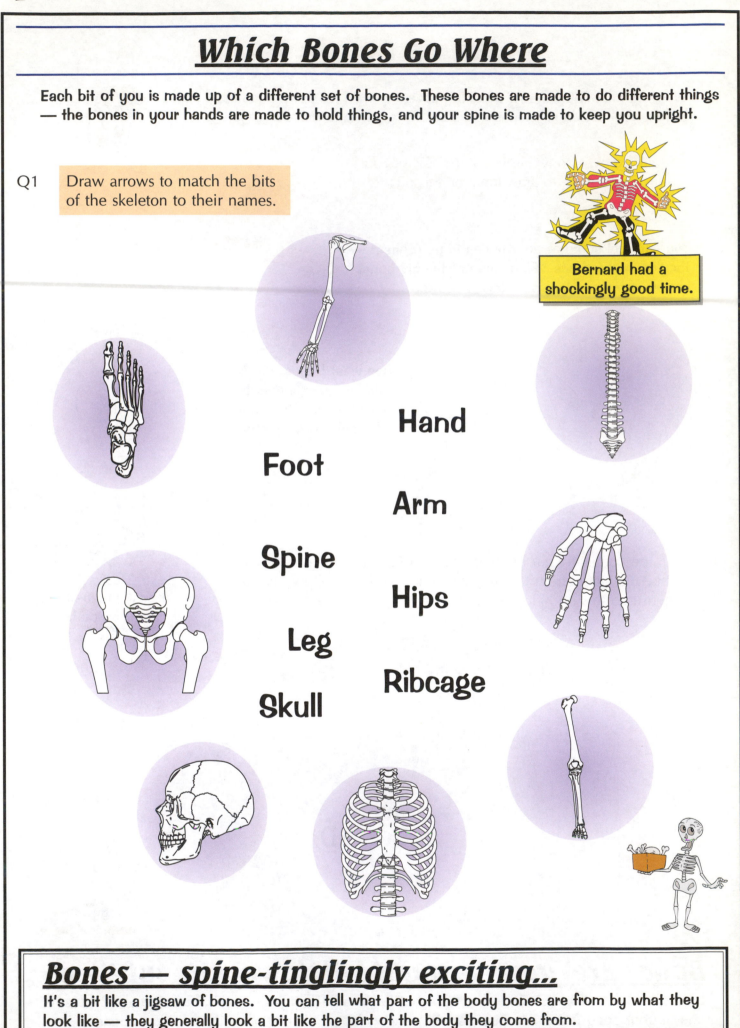

Bernard had a shockingly good time.

Hand

Foot

Arm

Spine

Hips

Leg

Ribcage

Skull

Bones — spine-tinglingly exciting...

It's a bit like a jigsaw of bones. You can tell what part of the body bones are from by what they look like — they generally look a bit like the part of the body they come from.

Which Bones Go Where

Show how much you know about skeletons — spot the missing pieces and draw them in.

Q1   Draw the missing pieces on to the skeleton to complete the picture — but watch out, you don't need all of them.

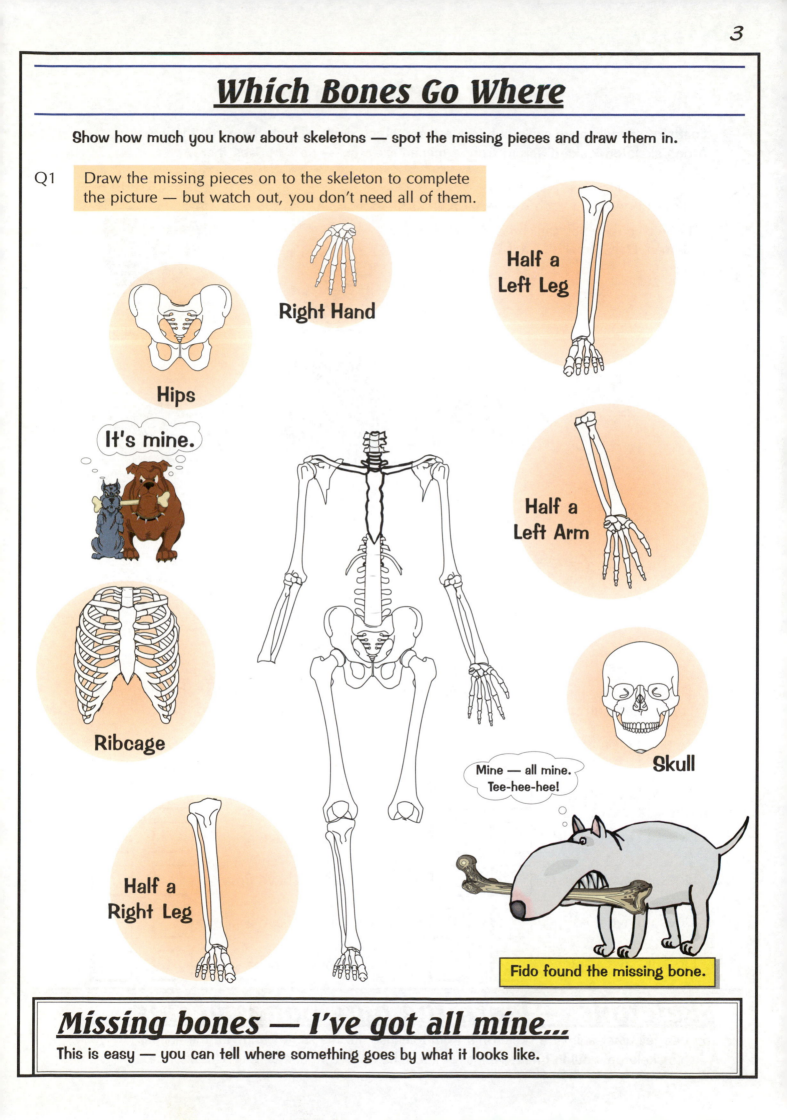

Right Hand

Half a Left Leg

Hips

It's mine.

Half a Left Arm

Ribcage

Mine — all mine. Tee-hee-hee!

Skull

Half a Right Leg

Fido found the missing bone.

Missing bones — I've got all mine...

This is easy — you can tell where something goes by what it looks like.

4

Skeletons

Loads of animals have skeletons inside them. They don't all look the same though.
A dog skeleton looks different from a human skeleton — no surprises there.

Q1 Have a look at these skeletons.
Write underneath each one what animal it's from.

To help you out, you can choose from this list:
Human, Dog, Bird, Fish, Frog, Lizard

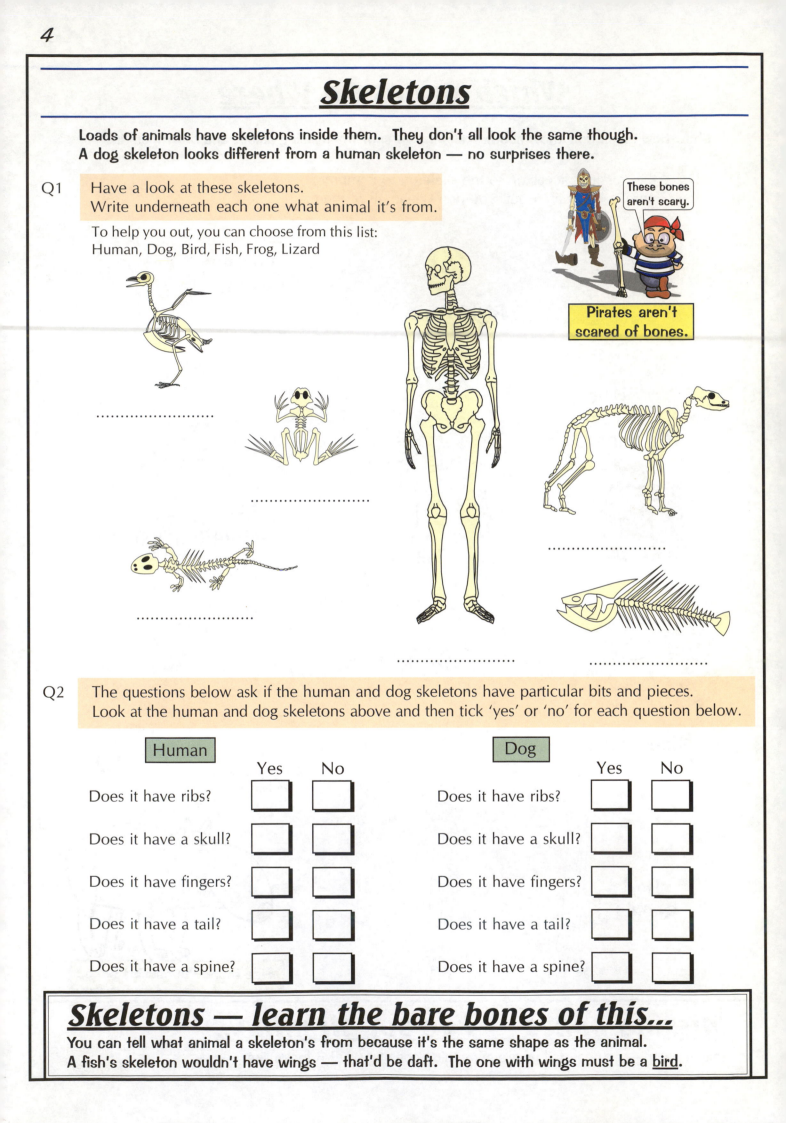

These bones aren't scary.

Pirates aren't scared of bones.

....

....

....

....

....

....

Q2 The questions below ask if the human and dog skeletons have particular bits and pieces.
Look at the human and dog skeletons above and then tick 'yes' or 'no' for each question below.

Human	Yes	No
Does it have ribs?	☐	☐
Does it have a skull?	☐	☐
Does it have fingers?	☐	☐
Does it have a tail?	☐	☐
Does it have a spine?	☐	☐

Dog	Yes	No
Does it have ribs?	☐	☐
Does it have a skull?	☐	☐
Does it have fingers?	☐	☐
Does it have a tail?	☐	☐
Does it have a spine?	☐	☐

Skeletons — learn the bare bones of this...

You can tell what animal a skeleton's from because it's the same shape as the animal.
A fish's skeleton wouldn't have wings — that'd be daft. The one with wings must be a <u>bird</u>.

Skeletons

Dinosaurs are great. You don't see them around any more — they all died out years and years ago. But by looking at their skeletons, we can figure out what they looked like.

Q1   Here are some dinosaur skeletons.
Draw a line between each skeleton and the dinosaur it goes with. Watch out — you'll get a dinosaur left over.

Q2   There are animals around today that look a lot like some extinct animals would have done.

The woolly mammoth, which is now extinct, looked a lot like an animal that's alive today. Look at the four skeletons of living animals and write down the one that looks most like the mammoth.

Dog

Horse

Mammoth

The mammoth looks like ....

Elephant

Fish

I'm not budging. What are you going to do about it?

Mammoths didn't move for anyone.

Learning about dinosaurs — a mammoth task...

I bet you've seen those TV programmes with dinosaurs walking around. It's amazing — dinosaurs were around millions of years ago. They have to work out what they'd look like from skeletons.

What Bones Are Like

Bones are pretty important. Without them you'd be all floppy — like a great big jelly.

Q1 Look at these pairs of words and pictures. Tick which one of each pair is correct.

Bones are strong

OR

Bones are weak

This bone is better than sandpaper.

Bones are rough OR Bones are smooth

Bones are stiff

My old bones are so stiff

Hmmm.

OR

Bones are bendy

Great — A nice soft bed of bones!

Bones are soft OR Bones are hard

My mate's called John Bone — he's well hard...

You can tell whether bones are hard or soft, whether they're stiff or bendy and whether they're strong or weak by feeling them through your skin. That makes this page a lot easier.

Broken Bones

Bones are strong, but they're also brittle — this means that they can break.
Doctors use X-rays to look inside the body — so they can see if any bones are broken.

Q1   Daft Doctor Felicity Peabrain has muddled up her patients' X-rays.
Match each patient to their own X-ray by drawing a line between them.

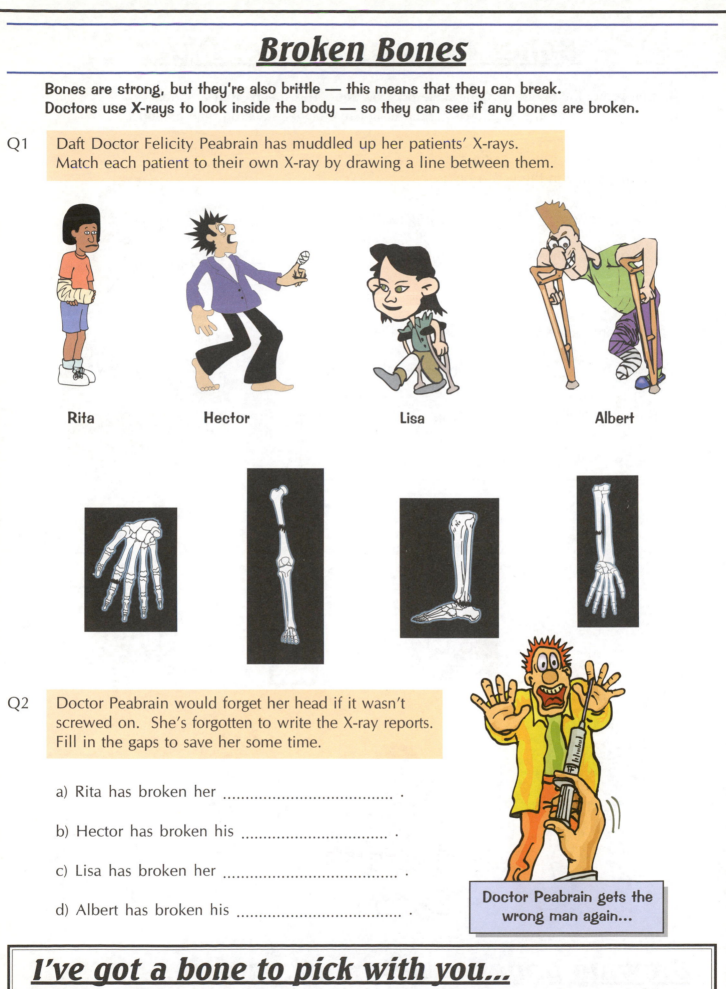

Rita   **Hector**   **Lisa**   **Albert**

Q2   Doctor Peabrain would forget her head if it wasn't
screwed on. She's forgotten to write the X-ray reports.
Fill in the gaps to save her some time.

a) Rita has broken her ....

b) Hector has broken his ....

c) Lisa has broken her ....

d) Albert has broken his ....

Doctor Peabrain gets the
wrong man again...

I've got a bone to pick with you...

Don't panic. You don't have to know the name of every single bone. Just make sure you know
which ones the skull, the spine and the ribs are. Only doctors need to know the names of the rest.

8

Bones Grow as You Get Older

As you grow, the bones of your skeleton grow too. This means that an adult has a bigger skeleton than a child, and a child has a bigger skeleton than a baby.

Q1   Fill in the gaps in the sentences below.
Use the words in the green box.

As you grow .... and bigger, the ....

of your skeleton also grow. Adults have ....

bones than children. But not all the bones ....

at the same speed. Some bones, like the ....,

grow more .... than some other bones.

slowly	skull	bigger
grow	older	bones

Hilary's bones grow at different speeds.

Q2   Match the different skeletons with the pictures of the baby, girl and the man. Put the right letters in the boxes by the skeletons.

Growing bones — not in my garden...

All your bones grow as you get older — that's why a grown-up is bigger than a baby. Some bones grow faster than others — your skull grows really slowly compared to your leg bones.

Bones Grow as You Get Older

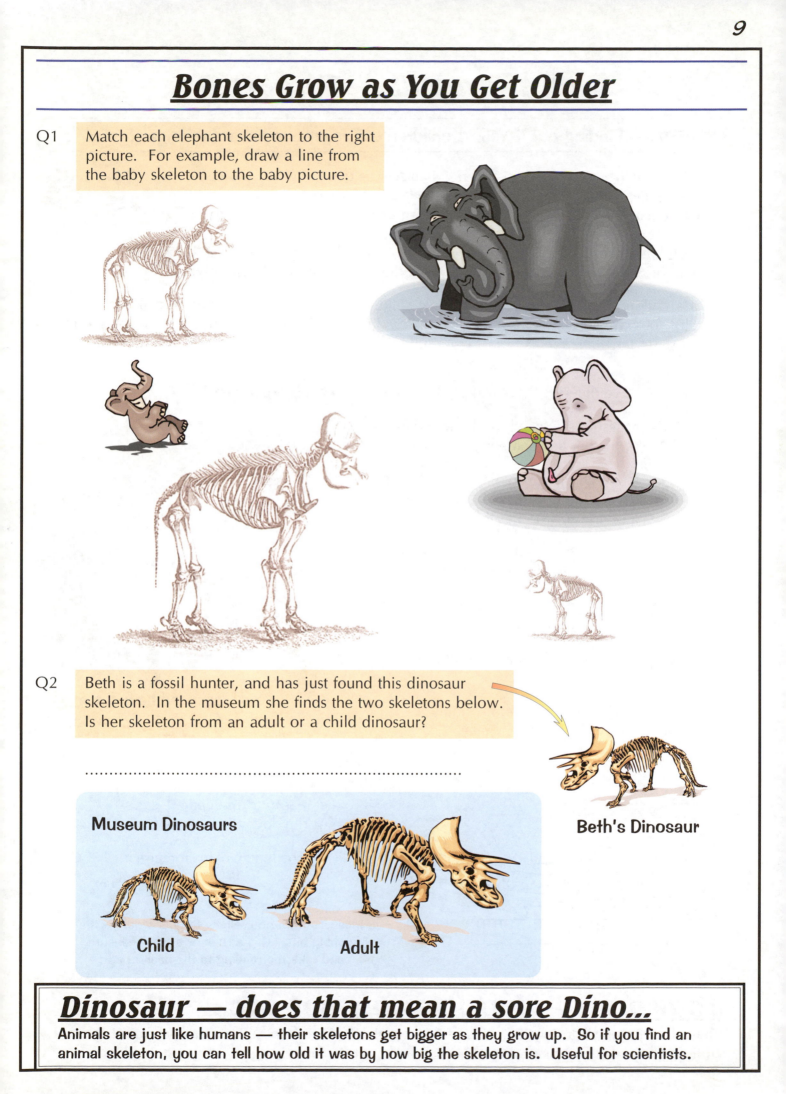

Q1 Match each elephant skeleton to the right picture. For example, draw a line from the baby skeleton to the baby picture.

Q2 Beth is a fossil hunter, and has just found this dinosaur skeleton. In the museum she finds the two skeletons below. Is her skeleton from an adult or a child dinosaur?

....

Beth's Dinosaur

Museum Dinosaurs

Child

Adult

Dinosaur — does that mean a sore Dino...

Animals are just like humans — their skeletons get bigger as they grow up. So if you find an animal skeleton, you can tell how old it was by how big the skeleton is. Useful for scientists.

Mini Project — Forearms

PROJECT — Finding out if Year 4 children or grown-ups have the longer forearms.

To <u>test</u> whether or not your skeleton gets bigger as you get older, you can do an <u>experiment</u>. You could measure the length of some forearms of Year 4 school pupils and then of some grown-ups.

This bit's the forearm.

Q1 You haven't done the experiment yet, so you can't know for sure what the answer will be. But you can make a guess. Tick the answer you think will be true.

Year 4 children's and adults' forearms are the <u>same length</u>. ☐

Year 4 children's forearms are <u>longer</u> than adults' forearms. ☐

Year 4 children's forearms are <u>shorter</u> than adults' forearms. ☐

Q2 Here are five different ways you could go about doing the experiment.

(A) Measure the length of the forearms of 1 adult and someone from Yr4.

(B) Get a group of some adults and some Yr4 children to stand in pairs, and just look to see who has the longest arms.

(C) Measure the length of the forearms of 30 adults and 30 Yr4 children.

(D) Measure the length of the whole arm of 30 adults and 30 Yr4 children.

(E) Measure the height of 30 adults and 30 Yr4 children.

Work out which way you think would be best, and write down the letter. ....

Look what I found!

That's cheating!

Rubbish plastic arm

Kev reckoned he had the longest forearm in the world...

Q3 Measure the length of <u>your</u> forearm, to the nearest cm. Write down the answer in the box.

The length of my forearm is

.... cm, to the nearest cm.

Measure from your elbow to your wrist — the knobbly bits. Use a ruler or a tape measure, and take the reading to the nearest cm.

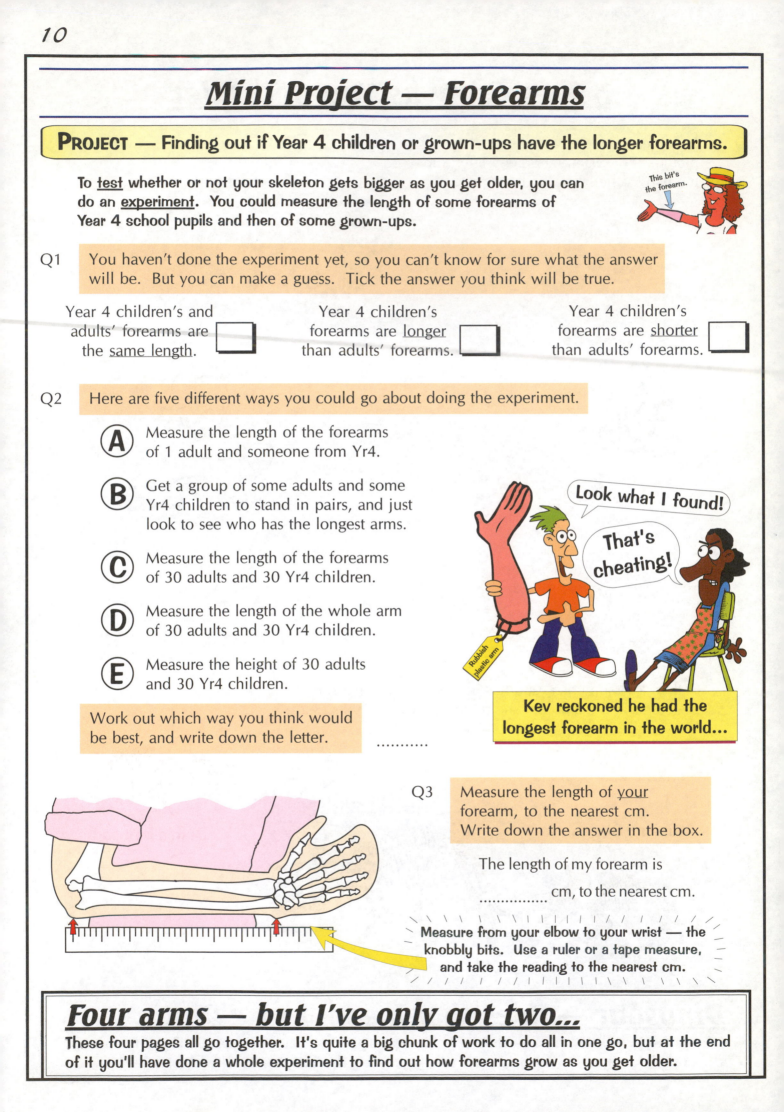

Four arms — but I've only got two...

These four pages all go together. It's quite a big chunk of work to do all in one go, but at the end of it you'll have done a whole experiment to find out how forearms grow as you get older.

Mini Project — Forearms

To find the result of the experiment, you need to get your ruler out and measure some forearms. You should write the lengths in a table, and then draw a pictogram afterwards. Start with these tables.

Q1 I've measured the forearms of 30 grown-ups for you. Go through the list of names and measurements, and fill in the frequency table. I've added up all the 23 cm ones for you.

Length of forearm, to the nearest cm	Tally	Frequency
23	⊬⊬⊬	5
24		
25		
26		
27		
28		

Lengths of 30 Adult's Forearms
(to the nearest cm)

Simon 25	Kat 26	Sheila 26
Angela 23	David 26	Glenn 26
Andy 25	Helen 24	Kay 25
Pat 24	Tim 25	Paul 27
Pula 26	Claire 23	Polly 25
Andrew 28	Charley 25	Louise 26
Gemma 23	Taissa 26	Linda 24
Ash 28	Chris 27	James 26
Gill 23	Stephanie 25	Viv 23
Lex 27	Iain 26	Lindsey 24

Q2 The best way for you to get the lengths of 30 Year 4 pupils' forearms is to measure the forearms of 30 pupils in your class.

If you can't find 30 Year 4 pupils, then you can use some or all of the spare numbers at the bottom of the page.

Use this space to write down each length after you measure it.

Don't forget to include your measurement from the last page!

Length of forearm, to the nearest cm	Tally	Frequency

Spare Numbers: 18, 17, 18, 16, 20, 19, 18, 17, 16, 15, 18, 19, 20, 17, 18, 17, 17, 19, 15, 16, 18, 18, 19, 17, 20, 16, 18, 19, 16, 18

Tally — isn't that what you watch cartoons on...

Make sure you get the measurements right, or the whole thing will be wrong.

Mini Project — Forearms

It can be tricky to work out what a bunch of numbers mean when they're in a table.
Draw a pictogram for each of the tables on p.11 to help you work out what's going on.

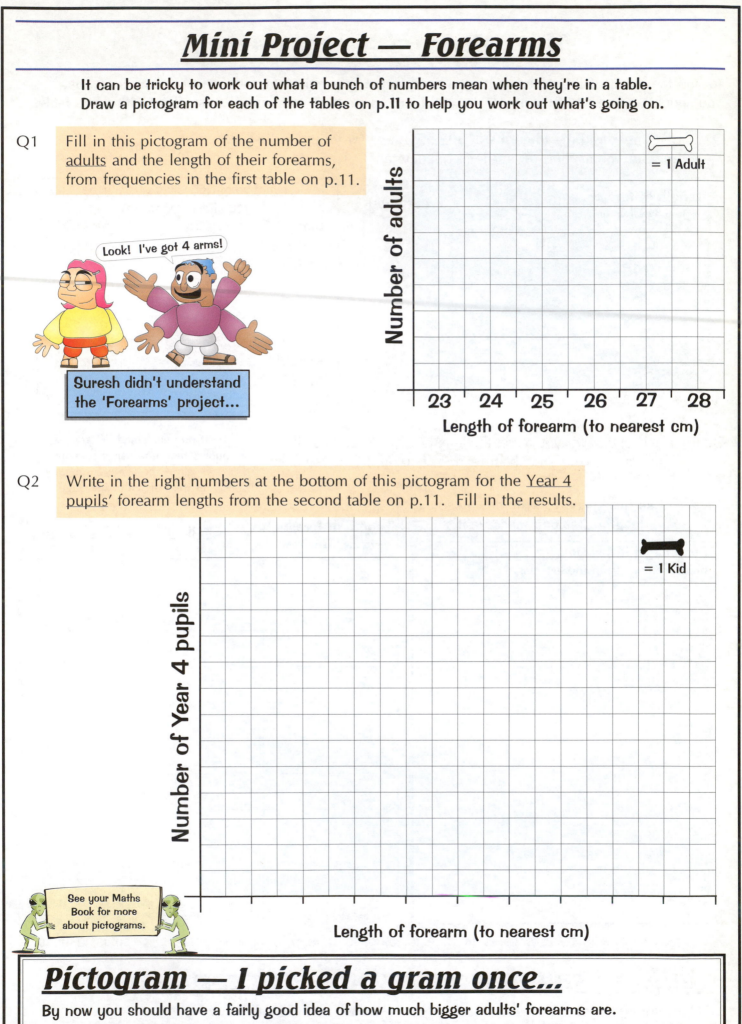

Q1   Fill in this pictogram of the number of <u>adults</u> and the length of their forearms, from frequencies in the first table on p.11.

= 1 Adult

Number of adults

23   24   25   26   27   28

Length of forearm (to nearest cm)

Look! I've got 4 arms!

Suresh didn't understand the 'Forearms' project...

Q2   Write in the right numbers at the bottom of this pictogram for the <u>Year 4 pupils'</u> forearm lengths from the second table on p.11. Fill in the results.

= 1 Kid

Number of Year 4 pupils

Length of forearm (to nearest cm)

See your Maths Book for more about pictograms.

Pictogram — I picked a gram once...

By now you should have a fairly good idea of how much bigger adults' forearms are.

KS2 Science Answers — Moving & Growing

Page 14 Change in Head Size

Q1:

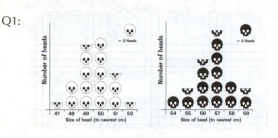

Q2: The most common head size for the group of year 4 pupils is 50 cm. The most common headsize for the group of adults is 57 cm. The head sizes for the adults are bigger. This suggests that as you get older your head/skull gets bigger/grows.

Page 15 Change in Leg Length

Q1:

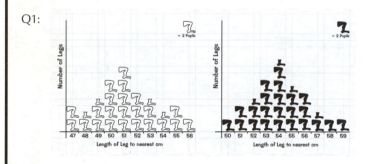

Q2: The most common leg length for the group of year 4 pupils is 51 cm. The most common leg length for the group of year 6 pupils is 54 cm. The leg lengths for the year 6 pupils are longer. This suggests that as you get older your legs get longer.

Page 16 The Skeleton Supports the Body

Q1: Internal skeleton: goat, elephant, fish
External skeleton: lobster, ladybird, grasshopper
No skeleton: slug, jellyfish

Page 17 The Skeleton Supports the Body

Q1: These joints should be circled. (Elbows, wrists, knees, (shoulders, hips), ankles.)

Q2: The slug, worm and squid should be circled.

Q3: Animals with skeletons are less flexible.

Page 18 Muscles and Bones

Q1: The top right arrow of both pictures should be coloured.

Q2: a) ➔ top muscle (bicep) b) ➔ top muscle (bicep)
c) ➔ bottom muscle (tricep) d) ➔ bottom muscle (tricep)

Page 19 Pairs of Muscles

Q1: a) this leg bends? Muscle 'B' will shorten and muscle 'A' will lengthen.
b) this leg straightens? Muscle 'A' will shorten and muscle 'B' will lengthen.

Q2: Muscles are attached to bones, and come in pairs. A muscle gets shorter to pull on the bones to move them. When one muscle in a pair contracts, the other muscle relaxes. The relaxed muscle also lengthens — it gets pulled by some of the moving bones.

Page 20 Pairs of Muscles

Q1: a) CONTRACTS b) HARD c) RELAXES

Q2: a) It will bend. b) Lengthen/relax
c) The arm will straighten.

Q3: a) TRUE b) FALSE

Page 21 Pairs of Muscles

Q1: The box on the right should be ticked.

Q2: It will bend even more.

Q3: The second box down should be ticked.
It will get shorter.

Page 22 Exercise and Rest

Q1: Measurements should be in the right boxes.
Numbers should be bigger after exercise.

Q2: 2nd time should take longer.

Q4: after

Page 23 Exercise and Rest

Q1: breathe faster slowly

Q2: a) ✓ x c) x ✓ e) ✓ x
b) ✓ x d) x ✓ f) ✓ x

Page 24 Revision Questions

Q1: arm foot ribs (ribcage) spine

Q2: Left, from top to bottom: fish, human child. Middle, from top to bottom: human baby, dog, frog. Right: human adult.

Q3: a) True e) False
b) False f) False
c) True g) True
d) False h) True

Q4: no skeleton internal skeleton external skeleton

Q5: The jellyfish

Page 25 Revision Questions

Q1:

Length of foot, to the nearest cm	Tally	Frequency
19	III	3
20	III	3
21	LHT I	6
22	II	2
23	I	1
24		0

Q2:

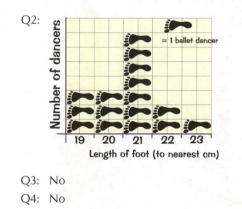

Q3: No

Q4: No

Q5: 'A' 'B' 'A'

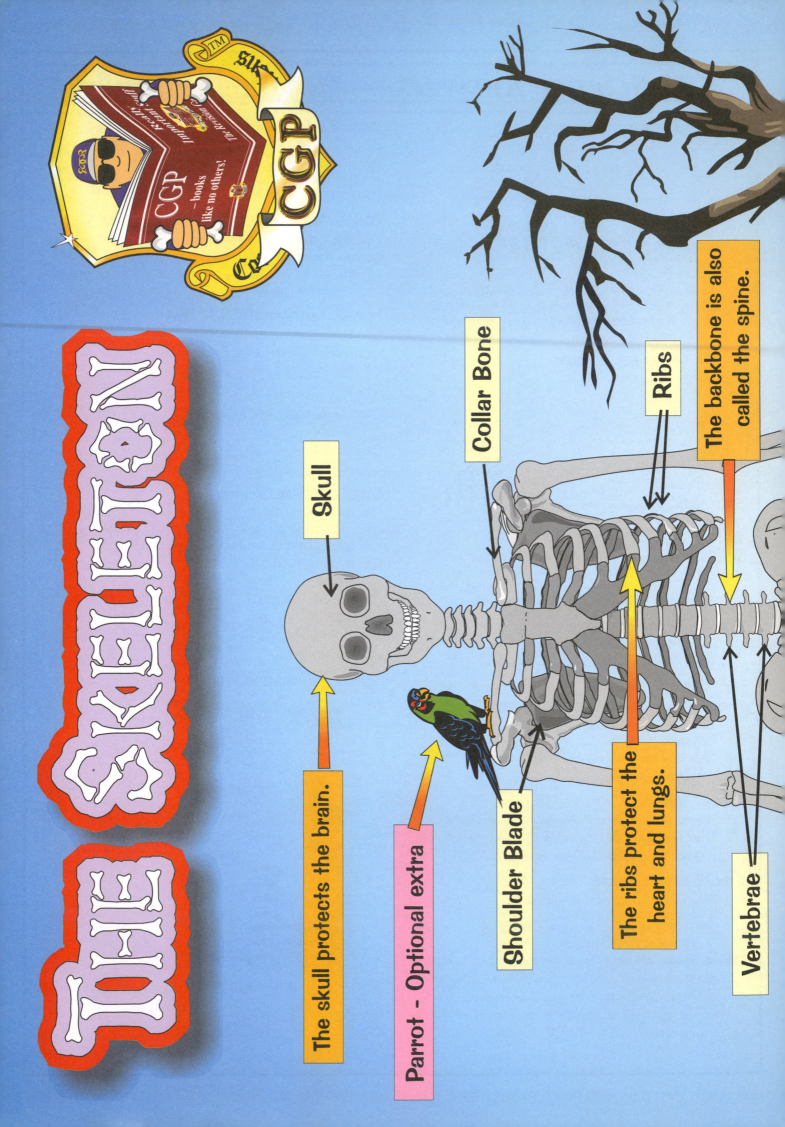

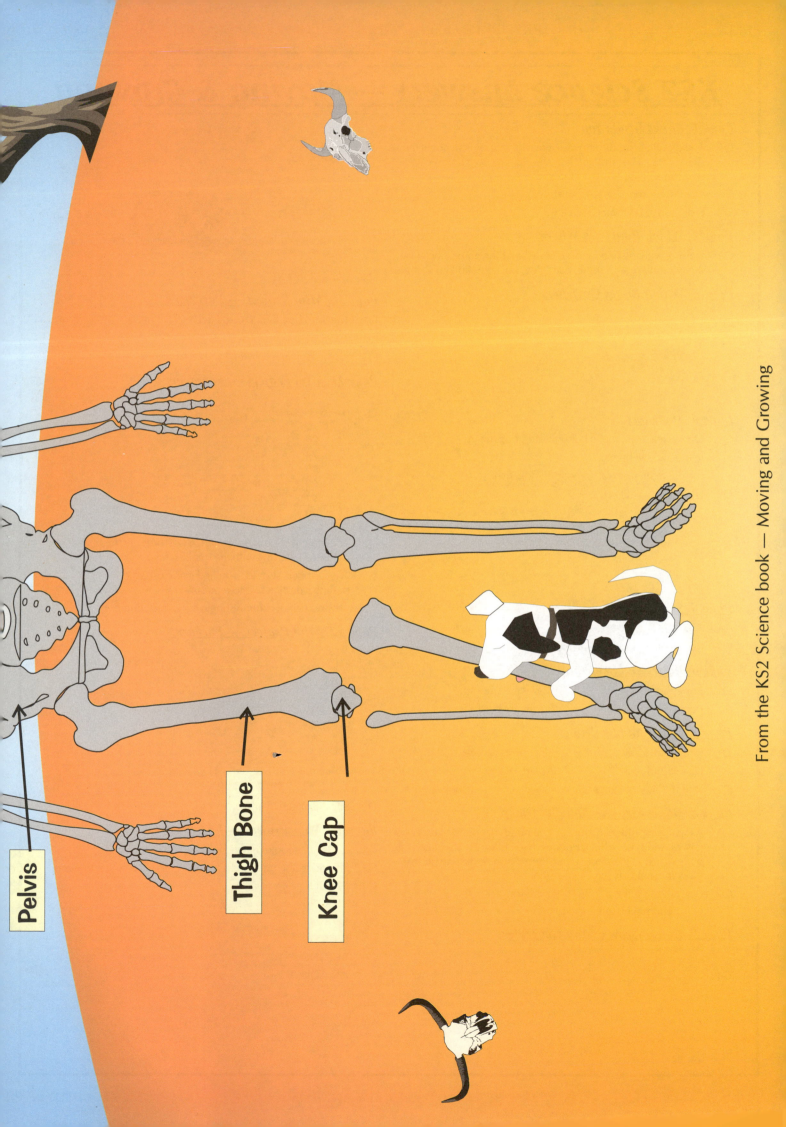

Pelvis

Thigh Bone

Knee Cap

KS2 Science Answers — Moving & Growing

Page 1 Bones Inside You

Q1: The drawings should show several ribs stopping in about the right place. The arms and legs should have two bones each, with gaps or joints at the elbows and knees.

  The fingers should have three bones each.

Q2: From top to bottom: C, A, D, B.

Page 2 Which Bones Go Where

Q1: Starting with the uppermost picture and then going clockwise the names are: arm, spine, hand, leg, ribcage, skull, hips, foot.

Page 3 Which Bones Go Where

Q1:

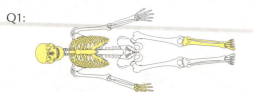

Page 4 Skeletons

Q1: On the left, from top to bottom: bird, frog, lizard.

  In the middle: human.

  On the right, from top to bottom: dog, fish.

Q2:

Human	Dog
yes	yes
yes	yes
yes	no
no	yes
yes	yes

Page 5 Skeletons

Q1: 1 → B   2 → C   3 → A

Q2: Mammoth — looks like **an elephant**

Page 6 Bones and Skeletons

Q1: Bones are strong ✓   Bones are smooth ✓

  Bones are stiff ✓   Bones are hard ✓

Page 7 Bones and Skeletons

Q1: Rita → 4th x-ray   Hector → 1st x-ray

  Lisa → 2nd x-ray   Albert → 3rd x-ray

Q2: a) arm   b) finger   c) leg   d) foot

Page 8 Bones Grow as You Get Older

Q1: As you grow **older** and bigger, the **bones** of your skeleton also grow. Adults have **bigger** bones than children. But not all the bones **grow** at the same speed. Some bones, like the **skull**, grow more **slowly** than some other bones.

Q2: A = tallest skeleton   B = top skeleton

  C = bottom skeleton

Page 9 Bones Grow as You Get Older

Q1:

Q2: Child dinosaur.

Page 10 Mini Project — Forearms

Q1: The third box should be ticked.

Q2: 'C'

Q3: Any reasonable answer.

Page 11 Mini Project — Forearms

Q1:

Length of forearm, to the nearest cm	Tally	Frequency
23	IIII	5
24	IIII	4
25	IIII II	7
26	IIII IIII	9
27	III	3
28	II	2

Q2: The lengths should be written in size order in the first column — starting with the smallest first.

  The numbers should be tallied in the usual way — putting a dash across to represent five.

  The frequency column should contain all numbers.

Page 12 Mini Project — Forearms

Q1:

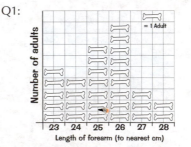

Q2: Should match their own results.

Page 13 Mini Project — Forearms

Q1: a) 26   b) Should match their results   c) adults

Q2: Should match up. Adults are bigger so have bigger forearms.

Q3: BIGGER

  BIGGER

  LONG

  BIGGER

  BIGGER

  AN ADULT

Mini Project — Forearms

You can look at the pictograms and work out what you think the <u>result</u> of the experiment is.

Q1 Fill in the gaps in these sentences, to show what the results of the experiment are.

a) The most common length of forearm for the adults is .... cm to the nearest cm.

b) The most common length of forearm for the Year 4 pupils is .... cm to the nearest cm.

c) The group of .... had the longest forearms.

> If there are two lengths which are the most common, just put the number in the middle (add them up and divide by 2).

Q2 Does what you've found out match up to what you said you expected in Q1 on p.10? Tick one box.

Yes ☐   **No** ☐   **Sort of** ☐

If it doesn't match up, say what's different, and give any reasons you can think of for why it didn't work out the way you expected.

....

....

....

....

Q3 Complete these sentences by circling the correct words in the brackets.

The experiment shows that your forearm gets (BIGGER / SMALLER) as you get older. If the forearm bones were the only ones that got (BIGGER / SMALLER), then adults would look daft with really (LONG / SHORT) arms. That's not true though, because the rest of the body gets (BIGGER / SMALLER) as well. That must mean that the <u>whole skeleton</u> gets (BIGGER / SMALLER) as you get older — until you're (9 YEARS OLD / AN ADULT).

Do adults or Year 4 pupils have the longest forearms?

FOUR pages on FOREarms — how FORtunate...

Right, that's it. You've finished the project. Now you know whether grown-ups or people from year 4 have longer forearms. I reckon you deserve a break after all that.

Change in Head Size

This is an experiment to test who has the biggest skulls, Year 4 pupils or adults.
I've measured 30 Yr4 children's heads and 30 adults' heads for you.
All you have to do is fill in the pictograms and work out what the result is.

Q1 Fill in the pictograms below, using the data from these tables.

Size of head to the nearest cm	47	48	49	50	51	52
Number of Yr 4 Pupils	1	4	9	10	5	1

I measured heads by wrapping a tape measure all the way round, just above the eyebrows — like when you measure someone's hat size.

Size of head to the nearest cm	54	55	56	57	58	59
Number of Adults	2	3	7	11	4	3

Pictogram of Head Size for a Group of Year 4 Pupils

= 2 Heads

Number of heads

Size of head (to nearest cm)

Pictogram of Head Size for a Group of Adults

= 2 Heads

Number of heads

Size of head (to nearest cm)

Q2 What do the pictograms show? Write down the results of the experiment here.

(HINT: Remember to say what the most common head size was for each group, and what it means about your head and your whole skeleton growing as you get older.)

....
....
....
....

Head size — no prize for being big-headed...

Since you know that the whole skeleton gets bigger as you grow up, you should find that adults have bigger heads. But after the experiment, you'll have some idea how much bigger.

Change in Leg Length

I wanted to know whether Year 4 children or Year 6 children have the longest legs, so I did an experiment. I got a group of 50 children from Year 4, and another 50 from Year 6, and I measured the length of their legs from the ankle to the hip, to the nearest cm. You have to work out what the result is.

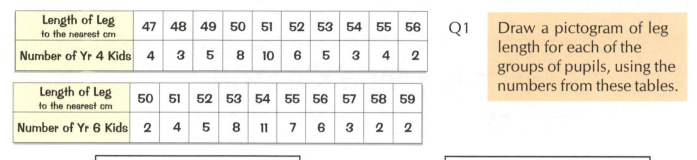

Length of Leg to the nearest cm	47	48	49	50	51	52	53	54	55	56
Number of Yr 4 Kids	4	3	5	8	10	6	5	3	4	2

Length of Leg to the nearest cm	50	51	52	53	54	55	56	57	58	59
Number of Yr 6 Kids	2	4	5	8	11	7	6	3	2	2

Q1 Draw a pictogram of leg length for each of the groups of pupils, using the numbers from these tables.

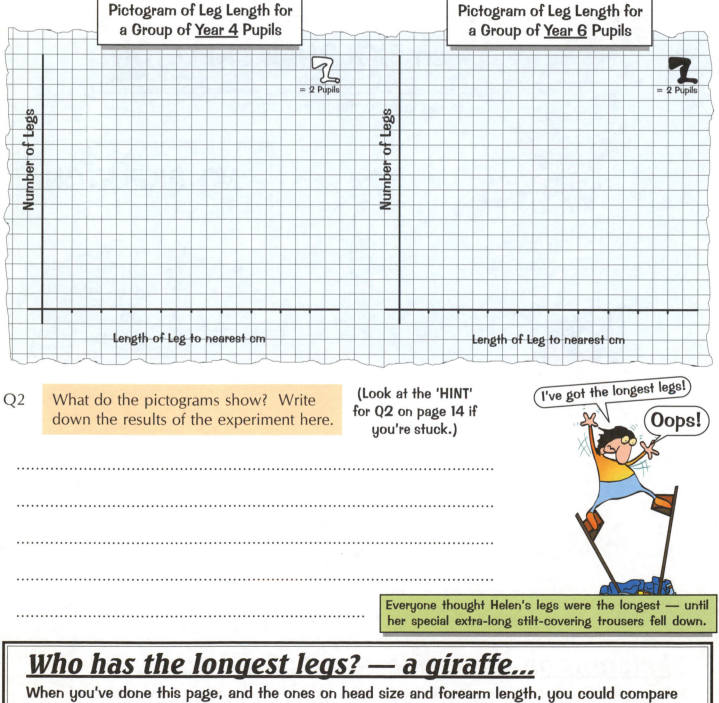

Pictogram of Leg Length for a Group of Year 4 Pupils

= 2 Pupils

Number of Legs

Length of Leg to nearest cm

Pictogram of Leg Length for a Group of Year 6 Pupils

= 2 Pupils

Number of Legs

Length of Leg to nearest cm

Q2 What do the pictograms show? Write down the results of the experiment here.

(Look at the 'HINT' for Q2 on page 14 if you're stuck.)

I've got the longest legs!

Oops!

Everyone thought Helen's legs were the longest — until her special extra-long stilt-covering trousers fell down.

....

....

....

....

....

Who has the longest legs? — a giraffe...

When you've done this page, and the ones on head size and forearm length, you could compare them all. You should find that all of them get bigger as you get older — no surprises there.

The Skeleton Supports the Body

Not all animals have skeletons <u>inside</u> their bodies. Some have skeletons <u>outside</u> their bodies — like a hard shell. And some don't have any skeleton at all — they're floppy or squidgy.

Q1   Write under each animal whether it has:

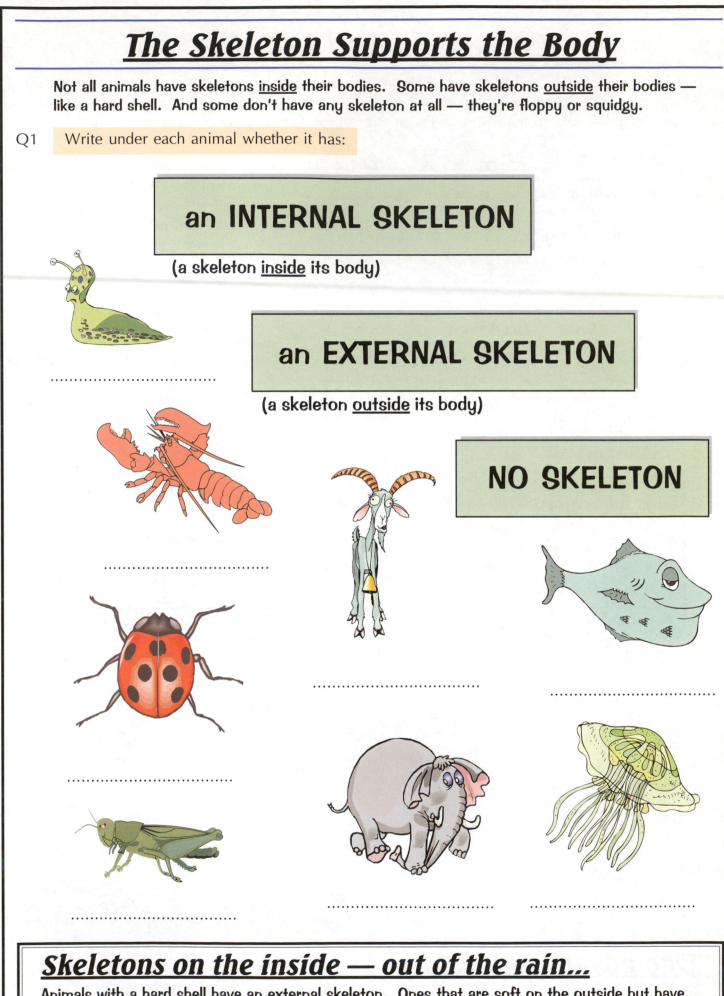

an **INTERNAL SKELETON**

(a skeleton <u>inside</u> its body)

an **EXTERNAL SKELETON**

(a skeleton <u>outside</u> its body)

NO SKELETON

....

....

....

....

....

....

....

....

....

Skeletons on the inside — out of the rain...

Animals with a hard shell have an external skeleton. Ones that are soft on the outside but have bones inside have an internal skeleton — like people. Some animals don't have any skeleton at all.

The Skeleton Supports the Body

Animals with skeletons can only bend where they have joints — joints are where two bones meet one another. But an animal with no skeleton can bend all over — which is pretty cool.

Q1 These animals all have internal skeletons. Circle the places on their legs and arms (if they have them) where they can bend. Don't worry about the joints in their fingers and toes.

Q2 Here are some animals that either don't have skeletons or have external skeletons. Circle the ones you think can bend all over.

Slug

Worm

Beetle

Scorpion

Squid

I'm flexible too - I hope...

Jane was testing her flexibility.

Q3 Do you think that having a skeleton makes an animal more or less flexible? Put a tick by the right answer.

Flexible is another word for bendy.

Animals with skeletons are more flexible. ☐

Animals with skeletons are less flexible. ☐

Friendly worms — bending over backwards to help...

So what it all comes down to is that skeletons make animals harder and less flexible. Animals with no skeleton are really flexible — like slugs or worms.

Muscles and Bones

Humans and animals have skeletons with muscles attached. When muscles work they get shorter and pull on the bones — this makes the animal move. Each muscle is attached to a different set of bones. You can feel your muscles change shape when you move.

Q1   Try bending your arms and legs. Feel which muscles are working. Colour in the arrows pointing to the right muscles.

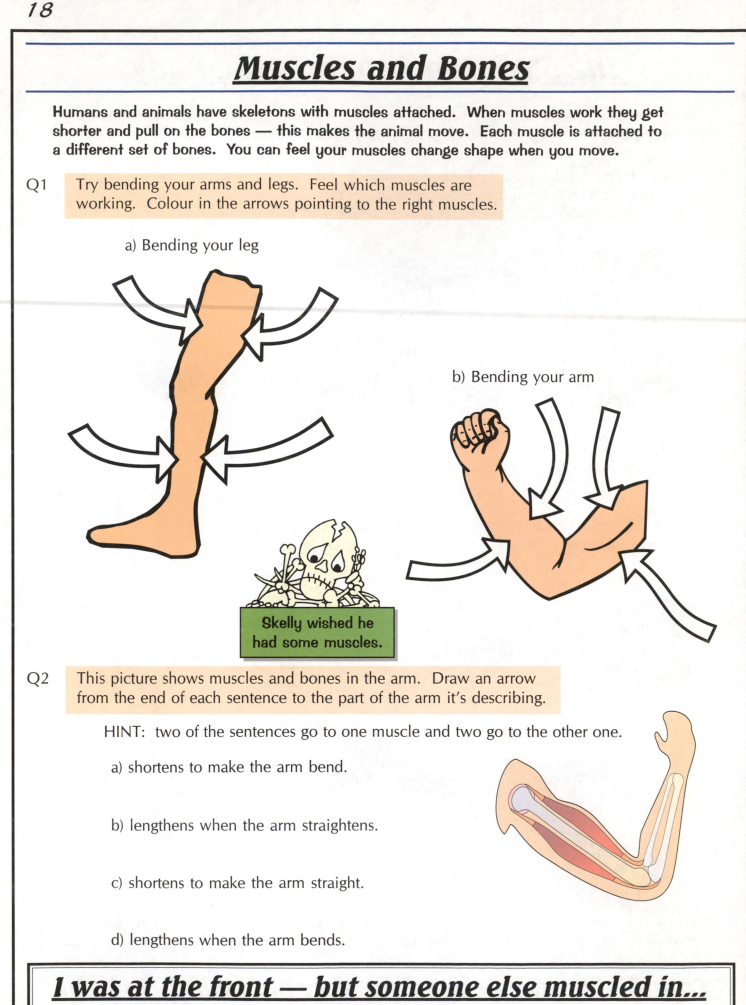

a) Bending your leg

b) Bending your arm

Skelly wished he had some muscles.

Q2   This picture shows muscles and bones in the arm. Draw an arrow from the end of each sentence to the part of the arm it's describing.

HINT: two of the sentences go to one muscle and two go to the other one.

a) shortens to make the arm bend.

b) lengthens when the arm straightens.

c) shortens to make the arm straight.

d) lengthens when the arm bends.

I was at the front — but someone else muscled in...

Phew, this stuff about muscles makes a change from all that stuff about bones. You need to know that muscles get shorter when they work — that's how they pull on your arm to bend it.

Pairs of Muscles

Muscles come in pairs. When one muscle contracts and shortens, the other muscle relaxes and lengthens back to its original shape.

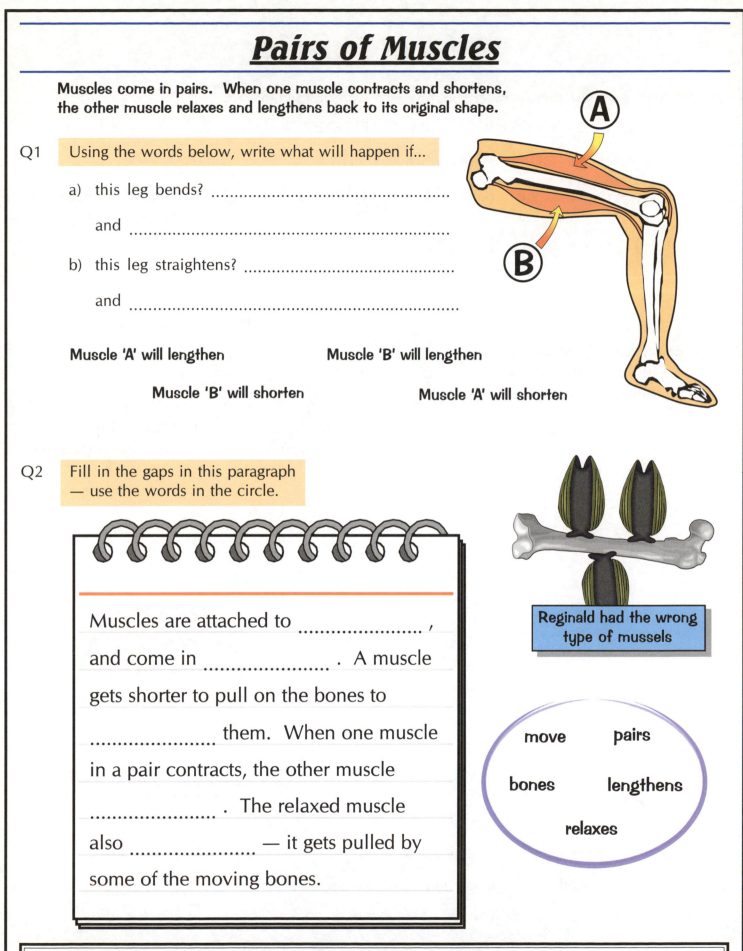

Q1   Using the words below, write what will happen if...

a) this leg bends? ....

and ....

b) this leg straightens? ....

and ....

Muscle 'A' will lengthen   **Muscle 'B' will lengthen**

Muscle 'B' will shorten   **Muscle 'A' will shorten**

Q2   Fill in the gaps in this paragraph — use the words in the circle.

Muscles are attached to .... , and come in .... A muscle gets shorter to pull on the bones to .... them. When one muscle in a pair contracts, the other muscle .... The relaxed muscle also .... — it gets pulled by some of the moving bones.

Reginald had the wrong type of mussels

move   pairs

bones   lengthens

relaxes

Pairs of muscles — and apples of muscles...

OK, so muscles come in pairs, like trousers or scissors. Like in your arm — you use one to bend it and the other one to straighten it. When one gets shorter, the other one gets longer.

Pairs of Muscles

Q1   Complete the sentences by circling the right word in the brackets.

a) When a muscle works, it (CONTRACTS / RELAXES).

b) A muscle gets (SOFT / HARD) when it shortens.

c) When one muscle in a pair works and contracts, the other (ALSO CONTRACTS / RELAXES).

Q2   Muscles come in pairs to do opposite things.

This is a pair of muscles

The arm will bend if this muscle shortens.

a)   What will happen to the leg if this muscle shortens?

....

....

c)   What will happen if this muscle shortens?

....

....

b)   What will this muscle do when the other muscle shortens?

....

....

Billy overdid the body building!

Q3   Tick the right box after each sentence to say if it is true or false.

	TRUE	FALSE
a) Muscles work the same way in animals as they do in humans.	☐	☐
b) You only get one muscle on every bone.	☐	☐

Cockles and mussels, alive, alive-o...

I reckon it's pretty amazing that they know all this stuff. They know all about muscles, and how they come in pairs, and how they work together. It's one of the wonders of modern science. Wow.

Pairs of Muscles

You can tell when muscles are working and contracting — they change shape and become hard.

Q1 Tick the box pointing to the muscle that must go hard to make this arm straighten out.

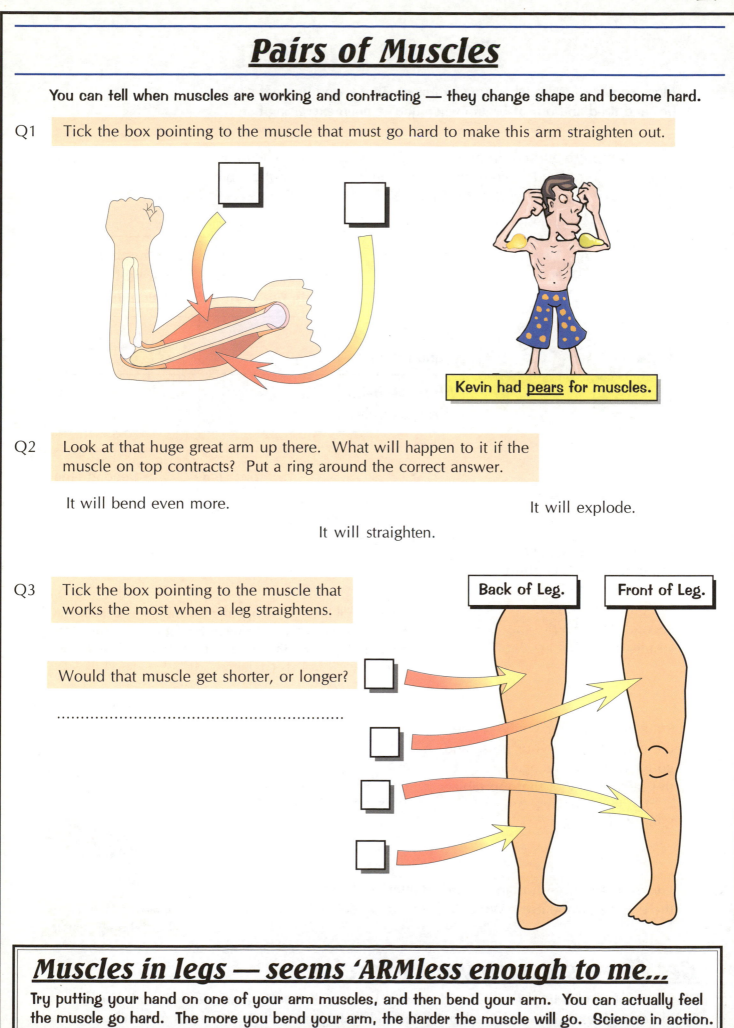

Kevin had <u>pears</u> for muscles.

Q2 Look at that huge great arm up there. What will happen to it if the muscle on top contracts? Put a ring around the correct answer.

It will bend even more.

It will explode.

It will straighten.

Q3 Tick the box pointing to the muscle that works the most when a leg straightens.

Back of Leg.

Front of Leg.

Would that muscle get shorter, or longer?

....

Muscles in legs — seems 'ARMless enough to me...

Try putting your hand on one of your arm muscles, and then bend your arm. You can actually feel the muscle go hard. The more you bend your arm, the harder the muscle will go. Science in action.

Exercise and Rest

Muscles work harder when you exercise. That's why you get all hot and tired and out of breath when you've been exercising hard.

Q1 Take your pulse and count how many times you breathe each minute when you're relaxed. Write the results in the first row of the table — the one that says "When I'm nice and relaxed".

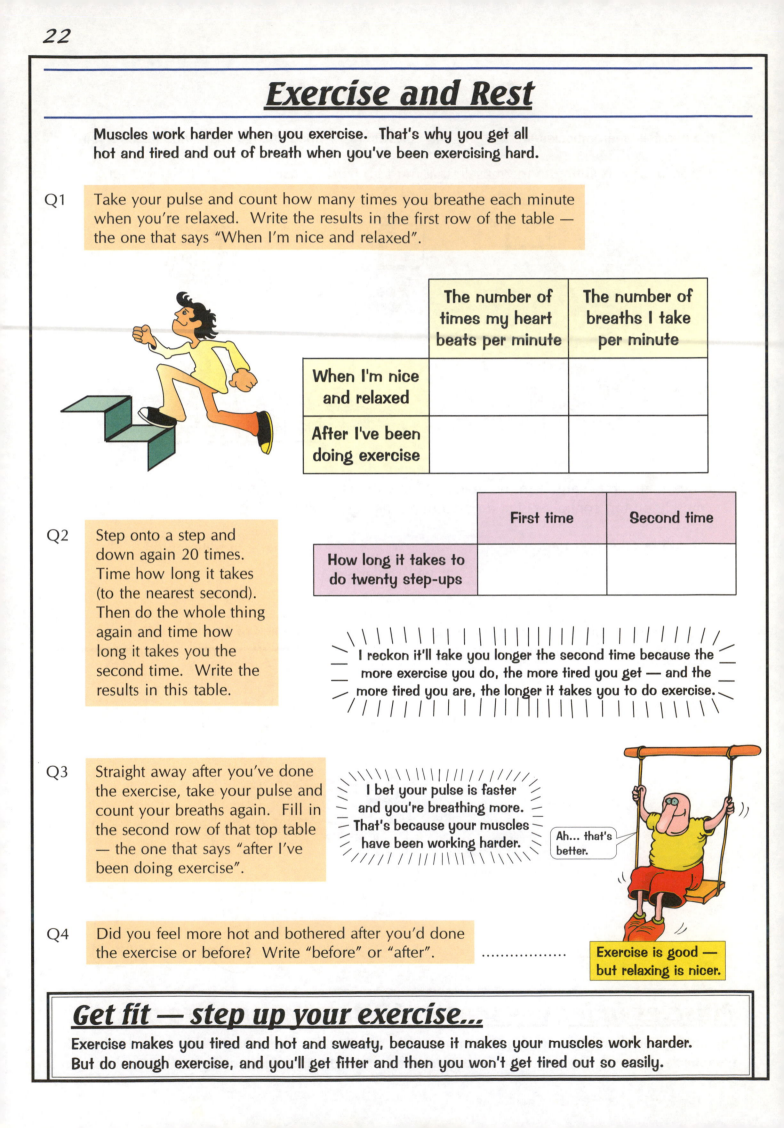

	The number of times my heart beats per minute	The number of breaths I take per minute
When I'm nice and relaxed		
After I've been doing exercise		

Q2 Step onto a step and down again 20 times. Time how long it takes (to the nearest second). Then do the whole thing again and time how long it takes you the second time. Write the results in this table.

	First time	Second time
How long it takes to do twenty step-ups		

I reckon it'll take you longer the second time because the more exercise you do, the more tired you get — and the more tired you are, the longer it takes you to do exercise.

Q3 Straight away after you've done the exercise, take your pulse and count your breaths again. Fill in the second row of that top table — the one that says "after I've been doing exercise".

I bet your pulse is faster and you're breathing more. That's because your muscles have been working harder.

Ah... that's better.

Q4 Did you feel more hot and bothered after you'd done the exercise or before? Write "before" or "after". ....

Exercise is good — but relaxing is nicer.

Get fit — step up your exercise...

Exercise makes you tired and hot and sweaty, because it makes your muscles work harder. But do enough exercise, and you'll get fitter and then you won't get tired out so easily.

Exercise and Rest

Have another look at the numbers you wrote in those tables on the last page.
Think about what they tell you about what happens when you exercise.

Q1 Use what you've learned to complete these sentences.

Choose from
these words

When you exercise, you .... more quickly than when you sit still.

When you exercise, your heart beats .... than when you sit still.

The more exercise you do, the .... you become.

faster

fitter

breathe

Exercising makes your muscles work hard. The faster you work, or the more weight you lift, the harder your muscles have to work. Stands to reason, really.

Q2 For each pair of people, put a tick underneath the person who is exercising harder.

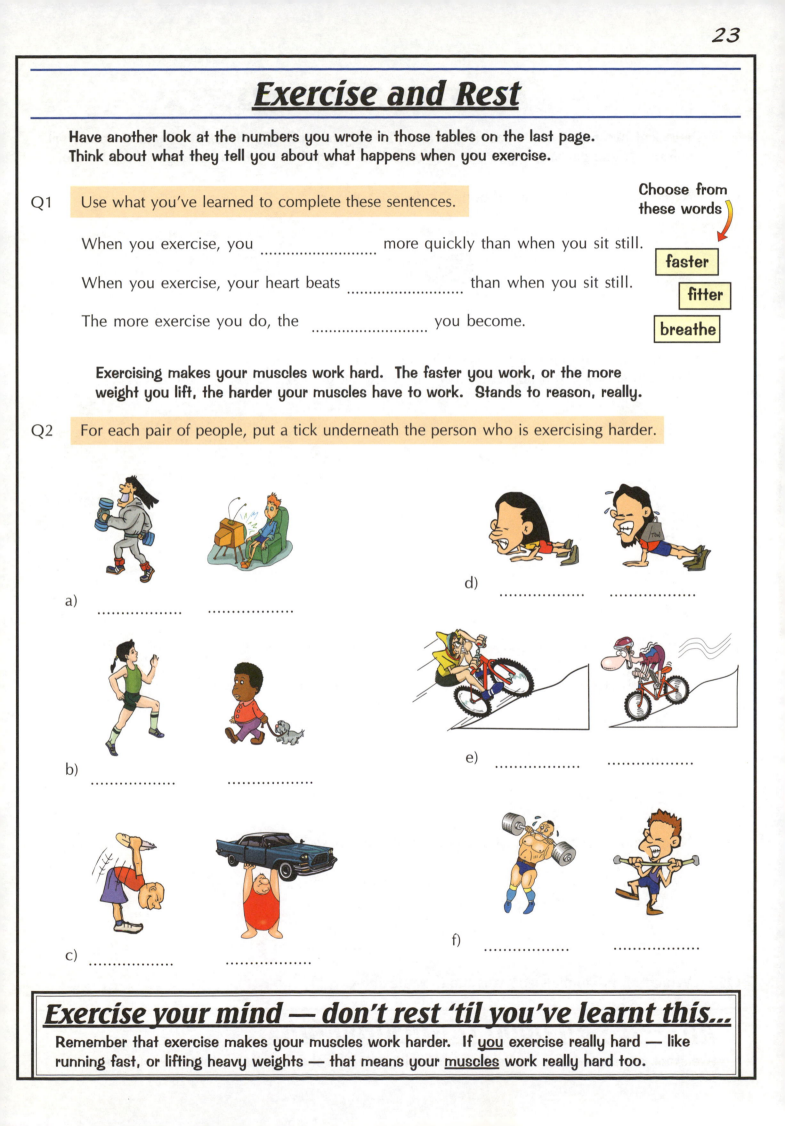

a) ....

b) ....

c) ....

d) ....

e) ....

f) ....

Exercise your mind — don't rest 'til you've learnt this...

Remember that exercise makes your muscles work harder. If <u>you</u> exercise really hard — like running fast, or lifting heavy weights — that means your <u>muscles</u> work really hard too.

Revision Questions

These last two pages are to test if you really know your stuff. Don't worry — you've done it all before. If you get stuck, you can flick back through the book and see how you did it before.

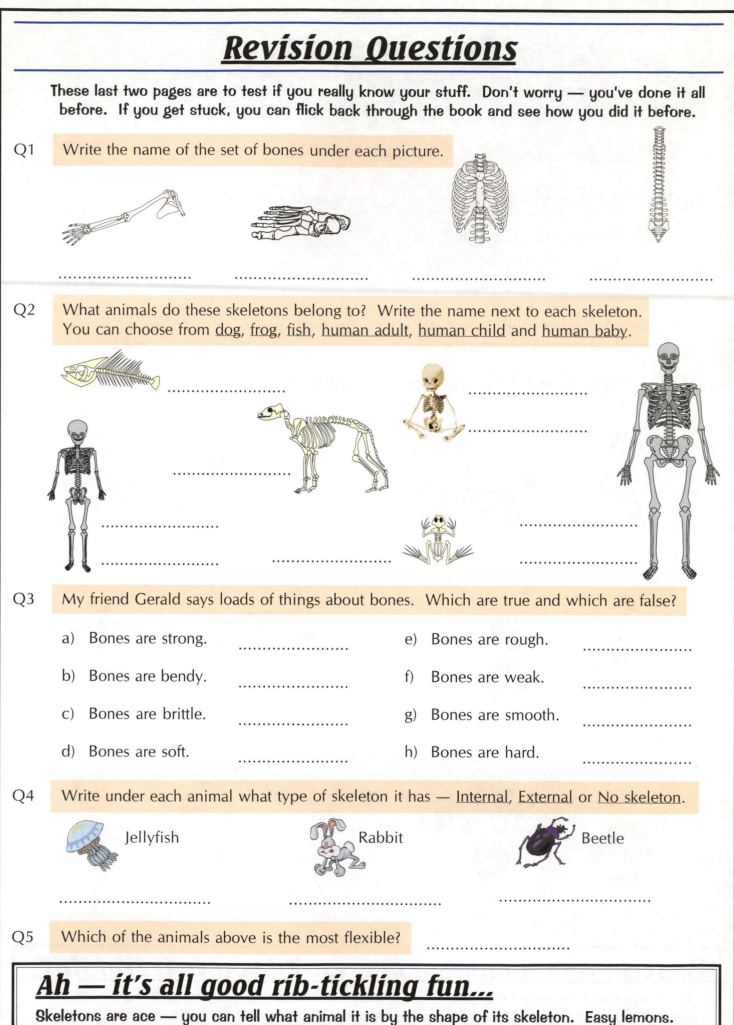

Q1   Write the name of the set of bones under each picture.

....

Q2   What animals do these skeletons belong to? Write the name next to each skeleton. You can choose from <u>dog</u>, <u>frog</u>, <u>fish</u>, <u>human adult</u>, <u>human child</u> and <u>human baby</u>.

Q3   My friend Gerald says loads of things about bones. Which are true and which are false?

a) Bones are strong.   ....   e) Bones are rough.   ....

b) Bones are bendy.   ....   f) Bones are weak.   ....

c) Bones are brittle.   ....   g) Bones are smooth.   ....

d) Bones are soft.   ....   h) Bones are hard.   ....

Q4   Write under each animal what type of skeleton it has — <u>Internal</u>, <u>External</u> or <u>No skeleton</u>.

Jellyfish   Rabbit   Beetle

....

Q5   Which of the animals above is the most flexible?   ....

Ah — it's all good rib-tickling fun...

Skeletons are ace — you can tell what animal it is by the shape of its skeleton. Easy lemons.

Revision Questions

Q1   I've measured the foot sizes of 15 famous ballet dancers for you.
Go through the list of names and measurements, and fill in the frequency table.

Length of foot, to the nearest cm	Tally	Frequency
19		
20		
21		
22		
23		
24		

Lengths of 15 ballet dancers' right feet
(to the nearest cm)

Dillon 22	Sheena 21	Craig 21
Wendy 19	Dominic 22	Ruso 19
Peter 21	Helen 20	Chris 20
Yeti 23	Jamie 21	Stephanie 21
Shiv 21	Sharon 19	Zita 20

Q2   Draw a pictogram to show how many <u>ballet dancers</u> have each <u>foot length</u>.
Use the frequencies in the table above.

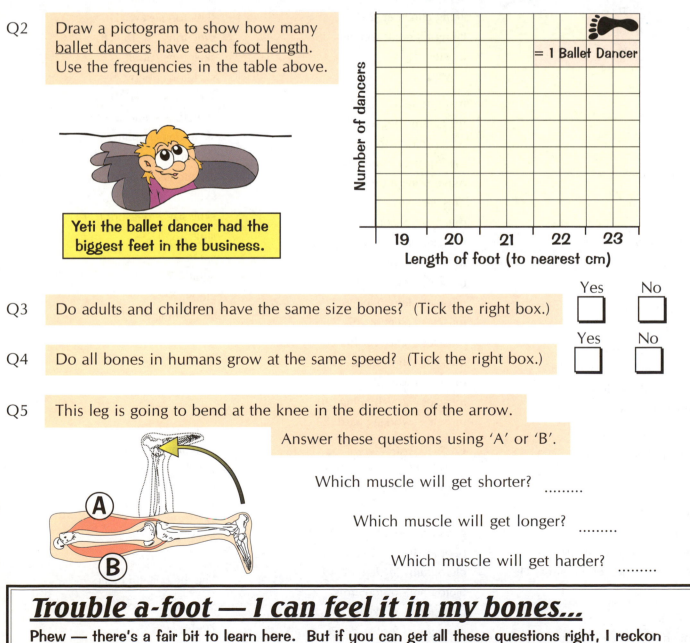

Yeti the ballet dancer had the biggest feet in the business.

= 1 Ballet Dancer

Number of dancers

19   20   21   22   23
Length of foot (to nearest cm)

Q3   Do adults and children have the same size bones? (Tick the right box.)   Yes ☐   No ☐

Q4   Do all bones in humans grow at the same speed? (Tick the right box.)   Yes ☐   No ☐

Q5   This leg is going to bend at the knee in the direction of the arrow.

Answer these questions using 'A' or 'B'.

Ⓐ

Ⓑ

Which muscle will get shorter? ....

Which muscle will get longer? ....

Which muscle will get harder? ....

Trouble a-foot — I can feel it in my bones...

Phew — there's a fair bit to learn here. But if you can get all these questions right, I reckon you'll be a bit of an expert at this movement and growth stuff. Time to sit back and relax...

Index